Lily's Story

by Linda Wyon

illustrations by Angela Goodman

Published in 2001 by
NACCC publications
National Association of Child Contact Centres
Minerva House
Spaniel Row
Nottingham
NG1 6EP

ISBN 0 9536548 4 2

NACCC would like to thank the Avon Probation Service and the Lord Chancellor's Department for funding the costs of printing and distribution of this book.

A British Library Cataloguing in Publication data. A catalogue record for this book may be obtained from the British Library.

Printed in the UK by Bath Press.

Foreword

Stories have always been a way of understanding our world, and storybooks for children can help parents to explain, and children to make sense of difficult ideas. Importantly, storybooks can be part of a shared activity between parent and child.

This book, by Linda Wyon with illustrations by Angela Goodman, captures in both the words and the pictures the important issues for parents and children caught up in the confusion and distress that can follow when parents separate. It highlights the role that Contact Centres can play in providing a safe environment which can help parents meet the challenge of sustaining and nurturing the relationship of the child with both parents, even when there is conflict or antagonism between the adults.

Lily's Story is an important partner to Ben's Story, Linda Wyon's previous book. This new book is aimed at younger children and their parents, and shows how small children often express their confusion and distress through behaviour rather than through words.

Dr Bob Potter
Consultant in Child and Family Psychiatry
Child and Family Therapy Service
Bath

This book is dedicated to my darling grandchildren

Jack, Chloe and Charlotte.

One fine day,
early in May,
Lily's Daddy
went away.

She looked in the bathroom,
She looked in the hall,

She looked
in the kitchen.

He wasn't there at all.

She looked in
the garage
where the
car used to be.
But Mummy's
old bike
was all that she
could see

Lily looked high,
Lily looked low,

Lily looked in the shed where Daddy used to go.

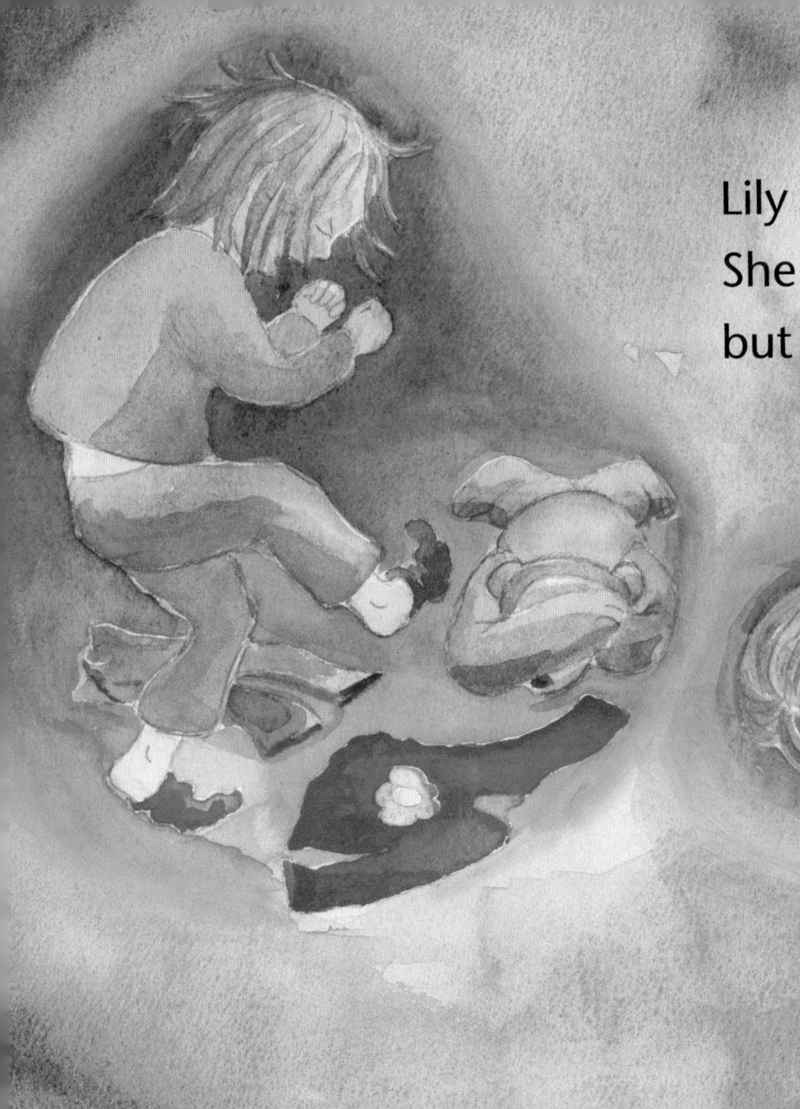

Lily felt bad, Lily felt sad,
She loved her Mummy,
but where was her Dad?

Lily would frown when they went into town.

Lily looked up,

and Lily looked down,

They went to a hall, where a lady with a book said, 'Come and have a look!'

They looked in the hall, with a man very tall...

...there were
children big and
children small.

The children there
made Lily stare,
they were playing with
their Daddies...
everywhere!

Late that night,
Lily went mad.
She cried and cried,

I WANT MY DAD!

'Wait till tomorrow', Mummy said, 'but now little Lily
it's time for bed.'

They went back to the hall,
with the man so tall
and the lady with the book
said, ‘Come and have a look...’

CONTACT
CENTRE
CHILDREN'S
ENTRANCE

They both went in and there was Dad.
Lily grinned, then ran, she was so glad.

They played and talked and Daddy kissed her.
She cuddled him.
He said he'd missed her.

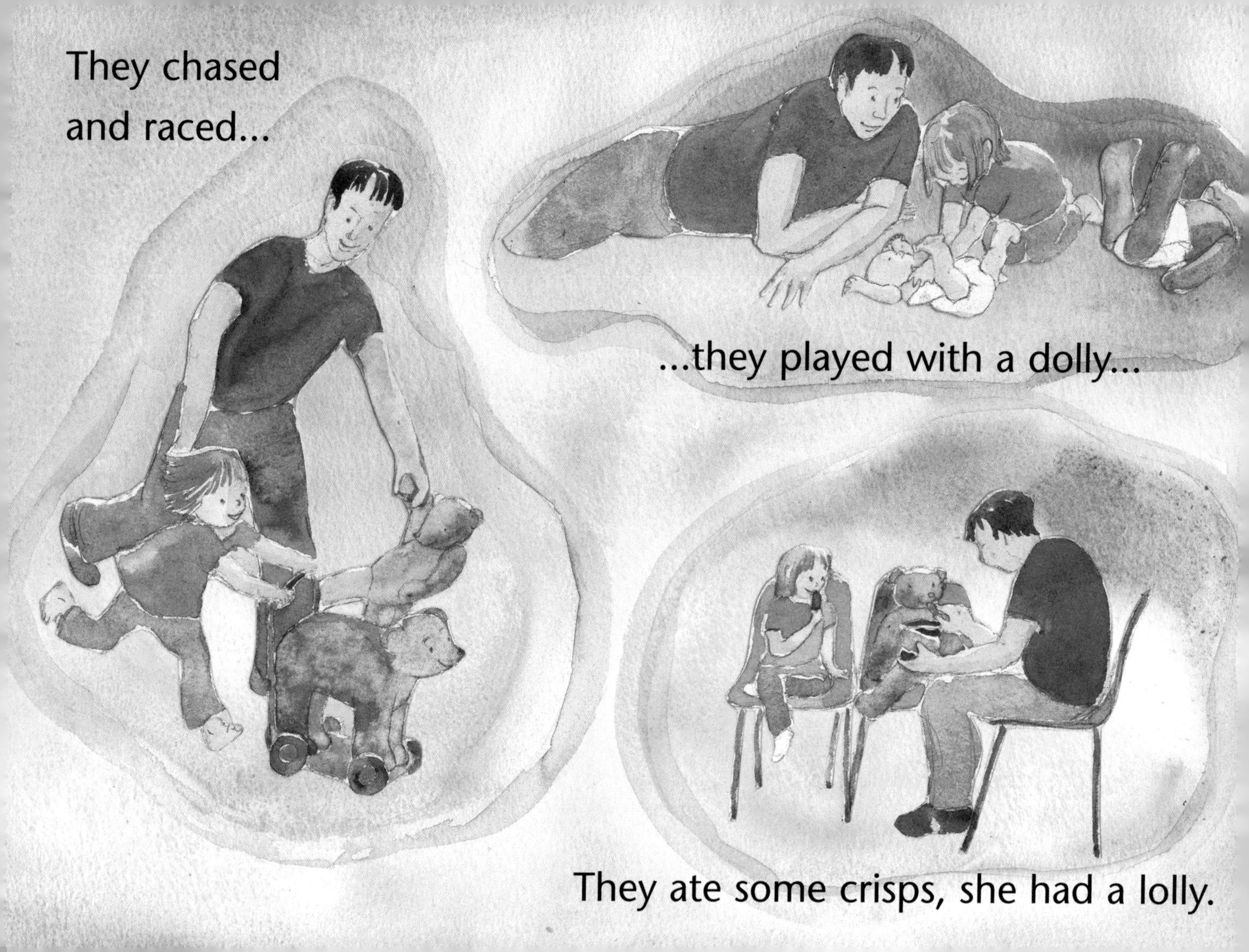
They chased
and raced...
...they played with a dolly...
They ate some crisps, she had a lolly.

They found some books and had some tea,
then she sat quietly on Daddy's knee.

'Lily my love, I do love you.'
'I know, Daddy, I love you too.'

One of the ladies said,
'Hello'.
Just five more
minutes,
then time to go.'

Daddy waved
goodbye, said,
'Come again
soon.'

and Lily went back to
the waiting room.

Lily skipped home
in the warm summer sun,
Lily and Daddy had
really had fun.

Lily's friend Jack
lives over the wall.

Jack's first Daddy left
when Jack was small....

He lives far away and his name's Paul
but he sometimes sees Jack at
The Contact Centre hall.

Lily no longer has to seek,

She sees her Daddy every week.

Mostly Lily's good...

sometimes Lily's bad...

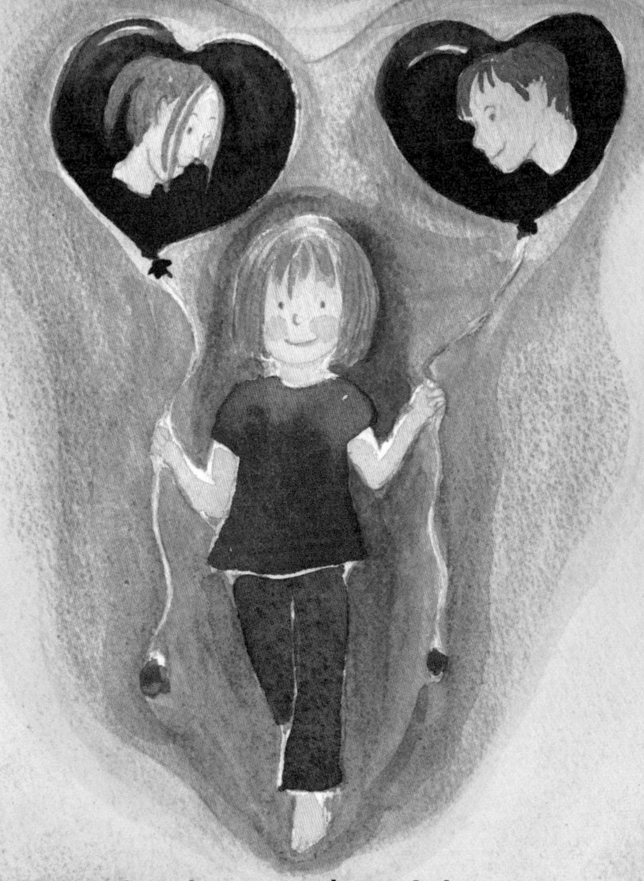

but she knows her Mummy loves her,

and so does her Dad.

Not all Centres are quite the same but if they belong to the National Association of Child Contact Centres they are all run to a National Code of Practice.

To find the telephone number of your nearest Centre please ring N.A.C.C.C. on 0115 948 4557